The
GREAT BIG BOOK
OF CHORUSES

Compiled by
David Culross

D1293552

Cat. #4672

SINGSPIRATION MUSIC
OF THE ZONDERVAN CORPORATION
GRAND RAPIDS, MICHIGAN 49506

1-86

86 87 88 89 90 / 20 19 18 17 16 15 14 13 12 11 10 9 8 7 6 5 4 3 2 1

This Is the Day

From Psalm 118: 24

Traditional
Arr. by David Culross

We Have Come into His House

B.B.

BRUCE BALLINGER

1. We have come in - to His house and gath -ered in His name to
2. So for - get a - bout your-self and con - cen-trate on Him and
3. Let us lift up ho - ly hands and mag - ni - fy His name and

wor - ship Him,_____ We have come in - to His house and
wor - ship Him,_____ So for - get a - bout your-self and
wor - ship Him,_____ Let us lift up ho - ly hands and

gath -ered in His name to wor - ship Him;_____ We have
con -cen-trate on Him and wor - ship Him;_____ So for -
mag - ni - fy His name and wor - ship Him;_____ Let us

come in - to His house and gath - ered in His name to
get a - bout your - self and con - cen - trate on Him and
lift up ho - ly hands and mag - ni - fy His name and

wor -ship Christ the Lord.___ Wor-ship Him, Christ___ the Lord.___

Behold, What Manner of Love

P.V.

PAT VALENTINE

4

Teach Me, Lord, to Wait

From Isaiah 40:31

STUART HAMBLEN

They that wait up-on the Lord___ shall re - new their strength,___ They shall

mount up with wings___ as ea - gles;___ They shall run and not be wea - ry,

they shall walk and not___ faint: Teach me, Lord, teach me, Lord,___ to wait._____

Father, I Adore You

T.C.

TERRY COELHO

Three-part round, in unison

1. Fa - ther, I a - dore You, Lay my life be - fore You— How I ___ love You!
2. Je - sus, I a - dore You, Lay my life be - fore You— How I ___ love You!
3. Spir - it, I a - dore You, Lay my life be - fore You— How I ___ love You!

5

Thou Art Worthy

P.M.M.

PAULINE M. MILLS

Thou art wor - thy, Thou art wor - thy, Thou art wor - thy, O Lord, To re - ceive glo - ry, glo - ry and hon - or, Glo - ry and hon - or and pow'r. For Thou hast cre - a - ted, hast all things cre - a - ted, Thou hast cre - a - ted all things; And for Thy plea - sure

they are cre - a - ted— Thou art wor - thy, O Lord._____

I Know Who Holds the Future

A.B.S.

ALFRED B. SMITH

I know who holds the fu - ture And I know who holds my hand;

With God things don't just hap - pen, Ev - 'ry - thing by Him is planned;

So as I face to - mor - row With its prob - lems large and small,

I'll trust the God of mir - a - cles— Give to Him my all.

The Steps of a Good Man

From Psalm 37: 23,24

Source unknown
Arr. by David Culross

8

Day After Day

W.P.L.

WENDELL P. LOVELESS

Day af-ter day He loves me, and day af-ter day He
(D.C.) Day af-ter day He guards me— I need nev-er have a

leads; Day af-ter day He gra-cious-ly sup-plies my
fear; Day af-ter day He

needs, all my needs. tells me He is al-ways near.____

What tho the path be thorn-y, What tho the way be

long? What tho the sky be black, He____ fills my life with song!

9

Easter Song

A.H.

ANNE HERRING

Hear the bells ring - ing, they're sing - ing that we can be
Hear the bells ring - ing, they're sing - ing, "Christ is ris - en

born a - gain!
from the dead!"

REFRAIN

The an - gel up - on the tomb-stone said,— "He is

ris - en just as He said— Quick - ly now go tell His dis -

ci - ples that Je - sus Christ is no long - er dead!"

Joy to the world, He is ris - en, Al - le - lu - ia! He's ris - en, Al - le - lu - ia! He's ris - en, Al - le - lu - ia!___

I Believe in Miracles

CARLTON C. BUCK

JOHN W. PETERSON

I be-lieve in mir-a-cles— I've seen a soul set free; Mi - rac - u-lous the change in one Re - deemed thru Cal-va - ry! I've seen the lil - y push its way Up thru the stub-born sod— I be-lieve in mir-a-cles, For I be-lieve in God!

11

The Wonder of It All

G.B.S.
GEORGE BEVERLY SHEA

O the won - der of it all! The won - der of it all! Just to think that God___ loves me.___

O the won - der of it all!___ The won - der of it all! Just to think that God___ loves me.___

Peace Like a River

Traditional

*1. I've got   peace like a   riv-er, I've got   peace like a   riv-er, I've got   peace

*2. I've got love. . .   3. I've got joy . . .

Let's Just Praise the Lord

W.J. & GLORIA GAITHER

WILLIAM J. GAITHER

He Keeps Me Singing
a Happy Song

HOWARD STEVENSON

filled with song: I'm sing - ing, sing - ing, all day

filled with song: I'm sing - ing, sing - ing, all day

long! He keeps me all day long!_____

in tempo

long! He keeps me all day long!_____

Greater Is He that Is in Me

L.W.

LANNY WOLFE

Great-er is He__ that is in me, Great-er is He__ that is in me,

Great-er is He__ that is in me Than he that is in__ the world!

All Because of Calvary

W.P.L.

WENDELL P. LOVELESS

I All my sins are gone, All be-cause of Cal - va - ry; Life is filled with song, All be-cause of Cal - va - ry; Christ my Sav - ior lives, Lives from sin to set me free; Some day He's com - ing— O won - drous bless-ed day! All, yes, all be - cause of Cal - va - ry.

II All my sins are gone be-cause of Cal - va - ry; Life is filled with song be-cause of Cal - va - ry; Christ my Sav - ior Lives from sin to set me free;

The Greatest Thing

M.P.

MARK PENDERGRASS

17

We Shall Behold Him

D.R.

DOTTIE RAMBO

18

The Joy Song

Traditional
Arr. by Harry Dixon Loes

Him_____ Face to face,_____

_____ Our Sav - ior and Lord!_____

1. I have the joy,— joy,— joy,— joy— down in my heart

Down in my heart, down in my heart; I have the joy,— joy,— joy,— joy—

down in my heart, Down in my heart to stay._____

2. I have the peace that passeth understanding . . .   3. I have the love of Jesus, love of Jesus . . .

Faith in God Can Move
a Mighty Mountain

J.W.P. & A.B.S.

JOHN W. PETERSON & ALFRED B. SMITH

Faith in God can move a might-y moun - tain, Faith can calm the trou - bled sea, Faith can make the des - ert like a foun - tain, Faith can bring the vic - to - ry.

Whisper a Prayer

Source unknown

1. Whis-per a prayer in the morn - ing, Whis-per a prayer at noon,(at noon,)
2. God an-swers prayer in the morn - ing, God an-swers prayer at noon,(at noon,)
3. Je - sus may come in the morn - ing, Je - sus may come at noon,(at noon,)

C   G   C E⁷ Am⁷ D⁷   G C G

Whis-per a   prayer in the eve - ning To keep your heart in tune. (in tune.)
God an-swers prayer in the eve - ning To keep your heart in tune. (in tune.)
Je - sus may come in the eve - ning So keep your heart in tune. (in tune.)

No, Never Alone

Source unknown

No, nev-er a - lone, _____ No, nev-er a - lone, _____ He
prom - ised nev-er to leave me, He'll claim me for His own.

No, nev-er a - lone, _____ No, nev-er a - lone, _____ He
prom - ised nev-er to leave me, Nev-er to leave me a - lone.

Reflection of Your Love

J.L.   JIM LOUCKS

May Your love be re-flect-ed in me,____ May Your
love be re-flect-ed in me; May each day that I live be the
best I can give— May Your love be re-flect-ed in me.

My Desire

L.P.   LILLIAN PLANKENHORN

My de-sire____ to be like Je-sus, My de-sire____ to be like Him!____ His
Spir-it fill me,____His love o'er-whelm me; In deed and word ____ to be like Him.

Here Comes Jesus

Traditional
Arr. by David Culross

Here comes Je - sus, see Him walk-in' on the wa - ter;

He'll lift you up _____ and He'll help you to

stand. _____ O here comes Je - sus,

He's the mas-ter of the waves that roll, Here comes Je - sus,

He'll save your soul. _____ O here comes _____

Jesus Won My Heart

ALFRED BARRAT

HARRY DIXON LOES

Je-sus won my heart,____ Je-sus won my heart;____ By His love so
He won my heart, He won my heart;

full and free, And the grace He gave to me. Je-sus won my heart,____
He won my

Je-sus won my heart;____ By His love so full and free, Je-sus won my heart._
heart, He won my heart;

ad lib.

All Power Is Given unto Me

From Matt. 28:18

JAMES McGRANAHAN

All pow'r is giv-en un-to Me, All pow'r is giv-en un-to Me;

24

Go ye in-to all the world and preach the gos-pel, And lo, I am with you al-way.

Go Tell It on the Mountain

Traditional spiritual

Go tell it on the moun-tain, O-ver the hills and ev-'ry-where;

Go tell it on the moun-tain That Je-sus Christ is born!

1. When I was a seek-er, I sought both night and day; I
2. He made me a watch-man Up-on the cit-y wall, And

asked the Lord to help me, And He showed me the way.___
tho I am a Chris-tian, I am the least of all.___

Brighten Up Your Pathway
with a Song

A.A.L.

A. A. LUTHER

When the days are drear-y and the nights are dark and long, Bright-en up your path-way with a song; Just re-mem-ber Je-sus loves you, He can right the wrong, Bright-en up your path-way with a song.

Tho the world is filled with sor-row, God is on His throne; He will not for-sake you, for He car-eth for His own; Soon the sun will shine a-gain, take cour-age and be strong, Bright-en up your path-way with a song.

Sweet, Sweet Spirit

D.A.

DORIS AKERS

Sweet Ho - ly Spir - it, Sweet heav-en - ly Dove,
Stay right here with us, Fill - ing us with Your
love. And for these bless - ings We lift our hearts in
praise; With-out a doubt we'll know that we have been re-vived,
When we shall leave this place.

Above All Else

J.W.P.

JOHN W. PETERSON

A-bove all else_____ the world needs Je - sus,_____ As shad-ows fall_____
He is the best_____ of earth's pos - ses-sions,_____ A-bove all else_____
D.C.—*A-bove all else_____ the world needs Je - sus, A-bove all else_____*

_____ and hopes grow dim;_____ For He can lift a soul from dark de - spair,
_____ the world needs Him._____
_____ *the world needs Him._____*

Save from sin and an - swer prayer— There is not an - oth - er friend like Je - sus!_____

Come and Praise the Lord, our King

Sing chorus first and after each stanza

Traditional

Chorus: *Come and praise the Lord our King,* Hal - le - lu - jah!
1. Christ was born in Beth - le - hem, Hal - le - lu - jah!
2. He grew up an earth - ly child, Hal - le - lu - jah!
3. Je - sus died at Cal - va - ry, Hal - le - lu - jah!
4. He will cleanse us from our sin, Hal - le - lu - jah!
5. We will live with Him some day, Hal - le - lu - jah!

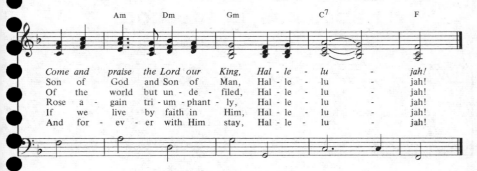

| Am | | Dm | | Gm | | | C7 | | F |

Come and praise the Lord our King, Hal - le - lu - jah!
Son of God and Son of Man, Hal - le - lu - jah!
Of the world but un - de - filed, Hal - le - lu - jah!
Rose a - gain tri - um - phant - ly, Hal - le - lu - jah!
If we live by faith in Him, Hal - le - lu - jah!
And for - ev - er with Him stay, Hal - le - lu - jah!

Cleanse Me

From Psalm 139: 23, 24

Maori melody

1. Search me, O God, and know my heart to - day; Try my, O
2. I praise Thee, Lord, for cleans - ing me from sin; Ful - fill Thy
3. Lord, take my life and make it whol - ly Thine; Fill my poor
4. O Ho - ly Ghost, re - viv - al comes from Thee; Send a re -

Sav - ior, know my thoughts, I pray. See if there be some wick - ed
Word and make me pure with - in. Fill me with fire where once I
heart with Thy great love di - vine. Take all my will, my pas - sion,
viv - al - start the work in me. Thy Word de - clares Thou wilt sup -

way in me; Cleanse me from ev - 'ry sin and set me free.
burned with shame; Grant my de - sire to mag - ni - fy Thy name.
self and pride; I now sur - ren - der, Lord—in me a - bide.
ply our need; For bless - ings now, O Lord, I hum - bly plead.

29

Happiness Is the Lord

I.F.S.

IRA F. STANPHILL

1. Hap-pi-ness is to know the Sav - ior, Liv-ing a life with - in His fa - vor,
2. Hap-pi-ness is a new cre-a - tion—"Je - sus and me" in close re-la-tion,
3. Hap-pi-ness is to be for-giv - en, Liv-ing a life that's worth the liv-in'

1. (to vs. 2)

Hav - ing a change in my be - hav - ior— Hap - pi-ness is the Lord.
Hav - ing a part in His sal - va - tion—
Tak - ing a trip that leads to heav - en—

2.

Hap - pi-ness is the Lord. Real joy is mine, no

mat - ter if tear - drops start; I've found the se - cret— it's

D.C. (to vs. 3) **3.**

Je - sus in my heart! Hap - pi-ness is the Lord.

Hap-pi-ness is the Lord. Hap-pi-ness is the Lord!

Pass It On

K.K. KURT KAISER

1. It___ on - ly takes a spark to get a fire___ go - ing,___
2. What a won-drous time is spring— when all the trees are bud - ding,___
3. I___ wish for you, my friend, this hap - pi - ness that I've___ found—

And soon all those a - round can warm up in its glow - ing;
The birds be - gin to sing, the flow - ers start their bloom - ing;___
You can de - pend on Him, it mat - ters not where you're___ bound;___

That's how it is with God's___ love, once you've ex - per - i-enced it;___ You
That's how it is with God's___ love, once you've ex - per - i-enced it;___ You
I'll shout it from the moun-tain top, I want my world___ to know:_ The

spread His love to ev - 'ry - one, you want to pass___ it on.___
want to sing, it's fresh like spring, you want to pass___ it on.___
Lord of love has come to me, I want to pass___ it on.___

Jesus Is the Sweetest Name I Know

L.L.

LELA LONG

Je - sus is the sweet - est name I know, And He's just the same as His love - ly name; And that's the rea - son why I love Him so— O Je - sus is the sweet-est name I know!

Lord, We Praise You

From Hebrews 13:15

OTIS SKILLINGS

1. Lord, we praise You. Lord, we praise You.
2. Lord, we love You. Lord, we love You.
3. Al - le - lu - ia! Al - le - lu - ia!

Wear A Crown

HARRIETTE WATERS

A. E. LIND

There's Something About That Name

W.J. & GLORIA GAITHER

WILLIAM J. GAITHER

Christd for Me!

A.B.   ALEX BURNS

Christ for me, Yes, it's Christ for me!

He's my Sav-ior, my Lord and King— I'm so hap-py I shout and sing!

Ev - 'ry day as I go my way It is Christ for me!

God Is So Good

Traditional
Arr. by David Culross

1. God is so good,_____ God___ is so good,_____

God___ is so good— He's so good to me.

Thy Loving Kindness Is Better than Life

From Psalm 63: 3,4

HUGH MITCHELL

1. Thy lov-ing kind-ness is bet-ter than life._____ Thy lov-ing kind-ness is bet-ter than life. My lips shall praise Thee, thus will I bless Thee;_____ I will lift up my hands un-to Thy Name._____
2. I lift my hands, Lord, un-to Thy name._____ I lift my hands, Lord, un-to Thy name. My lips shall praise Thee, thus will I bless Thee;_____ I will lift up my hands un-to Thy Name._____

To Be Like Jesus

Prayerfully

Source unknown

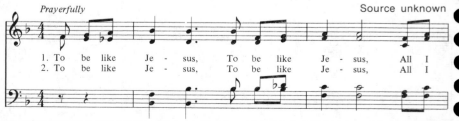

1. To be like Je - sus, To be like Je - sus, All I
2. To be like Je - sus, To be like Je - sus, All I

36

want,____ To be like Him;____ So pure and ho - ly, So meek and
ask,____ To be like Him;____ All through life's jour - ney From earth to

low - ly, All I want,____ To be like Him.____
glo - ry, All I ask,____ To be like Him.____

Stand Up and Tell It

Source unknown

1. Stand up and tell it if you love my Je - sus,
2. Go home and tell it if you love my Je - sus,

Stand up and live it if you love my Lord; I want to know,
Go home and live it if you love my Lord; They want to know,

I ought to know If you love my Lord.
they ought to know If you love my Lord.

Things Are Different Now

S.W.G.

STANTON W. GAVITT

Things are dif - f'rent now, Some-thing hap - pened to me When I gave my heart to Je - sus. Things are dif - f'rent now; I was changed it must be, When I gave my heart to Him. Things I loved be - fore have passed a - way, Things I loved far more have come to stay.

Things are dif - f'rent now, Some-thing hap - pened that day When I gave my heart to Him.

38

O What a Wonder

R.S.

RALPH SCHURMAN

O what a won-der that Je - sus found me, Out in the dark-ness no

light could I see; O what a won-der, He put His great arm

And won - der of won - ders,

un - der, And won - der of won - ders, He saved e - ven me!

The Good-bye Chorus

W.P.L.

WENDELL P. LOVELESS

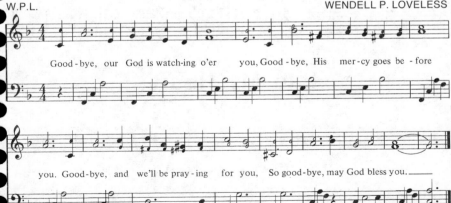

Good - bye, our God is watch-ing o'er you, Good - bye, His mer-cy goes be - fore

you. Good-bye, and we'll be pray - ing for you, So good-bye, may God bless you.___

Heavenly Father,
We Appreciate You

Traditional

1. Heav'n-ly Fa-ther, we ap-pre-ci-ate you._____ Heav'n-ly Fa-ther,
2. Son of God,___ we___ mag-ni-fy you._____ Son of God,___
3. Ho-ly Spir-it, what a com-fort you are._____ Ho-ly Spir-it,

we ap-pre-ci-ate you._____ We love you, a-dore you, We bow
we___ mag-ni-fy you._____ You've saved us from sin, gave a new
what a com-fort you are._____ You lead us, you guide us, You dwell

down be-fore you; Heav'n-ly Fa-ther, we ap-pre-ci-ate___ you._____
life with-in;___ Son of God,___ we___ mag-ni-fy___ you._____
right in-side us; Ho-ly Spir-it, what a com-fort you___ are._____

Into My Heart

H.D.C.

HARRY D. CLARK

In-to my heart, in-to my heart, Come in-to my heart, Lord Je-sus;

Come in to-day, come in to stay, Come in-to my heart, Lord Je - sus.

His Sheep Am I

O.J.

ORIEN JOHNSON

In God's green pas-ture feed-ing, by His cool wa-ters lie— Soft in the

eve - ning walk my Lord and I; All the sheep of His pas - ture fare so

won-drous-ly fine— His sheep am I.

{ Wa - ters cool, pas-tures
{ Dark the night, rough the
{ (In the val - ley,)
{ (In the val - ley,)

green, In the eve - ning walk my Lord and I;
way— Step by step, my Lord and I.
(on the moun-tain,) (In the eve-ning walk my Lord and I;
(on the moun-tain,) (Step by step, my Lord and Lord and I.)

Yesterday, Today, and Tomorrow

JACK WYRTZEN

DON WYRTZEN

Running Over

SETH SYKES

W. GARDNER HUNTER

Run - ning o - ver, Run - ning o - ver, My cup's
My cup's run-ning My cup's run-ning Glo - ry! my cup's

full and run-ning o - ver. Since the Lord saved me I'm as
Since the Lord saved me

hap-py as can be; My cup's full and run-ning o - ver.

Thy Word Have I Hid in My Heart

From Psalm 119

ERNEST O. SELLERS

Thy__ Word have I hid in my heart,_____ That I might not
in my heart,

sin a - gainst Thee;_____ That I might not sin, That
a - gainst Thee;

44

I might not sin, Thy Word have I hid in my heart.____

The Windows of Heaven

Traditional

The win-dows of Heav-en are o-pen, ____ The bless-ings are fall-ing {to - day;____ / to - night;____

There's joy, joy, joy in my heart, For Je-sus {has come in to stay;____ / makes ev-'ry-thing right;____ I

gave up my old tat-tered gar-ments,____ He gave me a robe of pure white;____ I'm

feast-ing on man-na from heav-en,____ and {Je - sus makes ev - 'ry-thing right.____ / that's why I'm hap-py to - night.____

Springs of Living Water

J.W.P.

JOHN W. PETERSON

Drink-ing at the springs of liv - ing wa - ter, Hap - py now am
Hap - py

I, My soul they sat - is - fy; Drink-ing at the
now am I, My soul they sat - is - fy; I'm

springs of liv - ing wa - ter, O won-der-ful and boun-ti -ful sup - ply!__

Isn't He?

J.W.

JOHN WIMBER

1. Is-n't He   beau-ti-ful?   Beau-ti-ful,   is-n't He?   Prince of Peace,
2. Is-n't He   won-der-ful?   Won-der-ful,   is-n't He?   Coun-sel - or, Al-

Happiness

W.J.G.

WILLIAM J. GAITHER

Altogether Lovely

W.P.L.

WENDELL P. LOVELESS

Al - to-geth - er love - ly, He is al - to-geth - er love - ly, And the fair - est of ten thou - sand, This won-der-ful Friend di - vine. He gave Him-self to save me, Now He lives in heav'n to keep me; He is al - to-geth - er love - ly, Is this won-der-ful Sav-ior of mine.___

With Eternity's Values in View

A.B.S.

ALFRED B. SMITH

With e - ter - ni - ty's val - ues in view, Lord, With e - ter - ni - ty's val - ues in view;

May I do each day's work for Je - sus With e - ter - ni - ty's val - ues in view.

Redemption Draweth Nigh

G.J.

GORDON JENSON

Signs of the times are ev - 'ry - where;_____ There's a brand - new

feel - ing in the air._____ Keep your eyes up - on the east - ern

sky;_____ Lift up your head, re - demp - tion draw - eth nigh.

He'll Break Through the Blue

D.W.

DON WYRTZEN

He'll break through the blue some-time soon, _____ Some morn-ing or night or noon; _____ He's com-ing to take us a-way _____ To heav-en's e - ter - nal _____ day. _____

Maranatha!

P.M.

PAUL MICKELSON

1. Mar-a - na - tha, _____ He is com - ing, _____ Mar-a - na - tha, _____ He is com - ing; _____ Mar-a - na - tha—
2. Mar-a - na - tha, _____ Come, Lord Je - sus, _____ Mar-a - na - tha, _____ Come, Lord Je - sus; _____ Mar-a - na - tha—

Com-ing back to catch His bride a - way!
E - ven so come quick-ly, Lord of

Lords!

In His Time

D.B.

DIANE BALL

1. In His time (in His time), in His time (in His time),
2. In Your time (in Your time), in Your time (in Your time),

He makes all things beau - ti - ful in His time (in His time).
You make all things beau - ti - ful in Your time (in Your time).

Lord, please show me ev - 'ry day as You're teach-ing me Your way,
Lord, my life to You I bring; May each song I have to sing

That You do just what You say in Your time (in Your time).
Be to You a love - ly thing in Your time (in Your time).

I'm So Happy

S.W.G.

STANTON W. GAVITT

I'm so hap-py and here's the rea-son why— Je-sus took my bur-den all a-way;___ Now I'm sing-ing as the days go by— Je-sus took my bur-den all a - way. Once my heart was heav-y with a load of sin, Je-sus took the load and gave me peace with-in;___ Now I'm sing-ing as the days go by— Je-sus took my bur-den all a - way.

Room at the Cross for You

I.F.S.

IRA F. STANPHILL

There's room at the cross for you,___ There's room at the cross for you;___ Tho

mil-lions have come, There's still room for one. Yes, there's room at the cross for you.___

The Bond of Love

Words from John 17:23 & Ephesions 4: 1-3

OTIS SKILLINGS

1. We are one in the bond of love; We are
2. Let us sing now,___ ev - 'ry - one; Let us

one in the bond of love.___ We have joined our spir - it with the
feel His___ love be - gun.___ Let us join our hands___ that the

Spir - it of God; We are one in the bond of love.
world will___ know; We are one in the bond of love.

God Can Do Anything but Fail

I.F.S.

IRA F. STANPHILL

God can do an-y-thing, an-y-thing, an-y-thing, God can
He can save, He can keep, He can cleanse, and He will, God can

do an-y-thing but fail.
do an-y-thing but fail.

He's the Al-pha and O-me-ga, the be-

gin-ning and the end, He's the fair-est of ten thou-sand to my soul;____ God can

do an-y-thing, an-y - thing, an-y-thing, God can do an-y-thing but fail.

Somewhere Beyond the Blue

A.B.S.

ALFRED B. SMITH

Some - where be-yond the blue there's a man-sion for me; Some-

where be-yond the blue I am long-ing to be; I'll see my Sav-ior's

face and sing of sav-ing grace, Some-where be-yond the blue, some day.

Whosoever Meaneth Me

J.E.M.

J. EDWIN McCONNELL

Who - so - ev - er sure - ly mean-eth me, Sure - ly

mean - eth me yes, sure - ly mean-eth me; Who - so - ev - er

sure - ly mean - eth me; Who - so - ev - er mean - eth me.
mean-eth me.

My Tribute

A. C.

ANDRAE CROUCH

To God be the glo - ry, To God be the glo - ry, To God be the glo - ry For the things He has done! With His

blood He has saved me, With His pow'r He has raised me— To
blood He has saved me, With His pow'r He has raised me— To

1.

To next strain

God be the glo - ry For the things He has done!
God be the glo - ry For the

2.

Fine

things He has done! Just let me live my

life— Let it be pleas - ing, Lord, to Thee; And should I

D.S.

gain an - y praise, Let it go to Cal - va - ry. With His

Let's Talk About Jesus

Traditional

Eb7   Ab   Ab7   Db   Bbm7

Let's talk a - bout Je - sus— the King of Kings is He. The Lord of

Eb   Eb7   Ab   Eb7   Ab

Lords su-preme___ thru all e - ter - ni - ty, The great I AM, the Way, the

Ab7   Db   Bbm7   Eb   Eb9sus Eb7   Ab

Truth, the Life, the Door— Let's talk a - bout Je - sus more and more.___

I Believe the Answer's on the Way

M.D.

MERRILL DUNLOP

I be-lieve the an-swer's on the way, I be-lieve the
Lord has heard me pray; "Cast not a-way your con-fi-dence," Saith the Lord our
God. Now by faith in Him a-lone I stand, Firm-ly held by
His al-might-y hand; Ful-ly trust-ing in His prom-ise, Praise the Lord!

Be Still and Know

Based on Psalm 46:10 & Exodus 15:26

Source unknown

Be still___ and know that___ I ___ am God. Be still___ and

58

know that_ I_ am God. Be still_ and know that_ I am God.

Saved to Tell Others

Hollywood Gospel Team

ARTHUR WOOLSEY

We're saved, saved to tell oth - ers of the Man of Gal - i - lee._

Saved, saved to live dai - ly for the Christ of Cal - va - ry._

Saved, saved to in - vite you to His sal - va - tion free._

rit.

We're saved, saved, saved by His blood for all e - ter - ni - ty._

Give Me Oil in My Lamp

A. SEVISON

Source unknown

60

Jesus Is Coming Again

J.W.P.

JOHN W. PETERSON

Com-ing a - gain,___ Com-ing a - gain;___ May be morn-ing, may be noon,

May be eve-ning and may be soon! Com-ing a - gain,___ Com-ing a - gain;___

O what a won-der-ful day it will be— Je - sus is com-ing a - gain!___

He Is Lord

Based on Phil. 2:11

Traditional

He is Lord, He is Lord! He is ris - en from the dead, and He is

Lord! Ev-'ry knee shall bow, ev-'ry tongue con-fess That Je - sus Christ is Lord.

Isn't He Wonderful!

Traditional
Arr. by Homer Hammontree

Is - n't He won-der - ful, won - der - ful, won -der - ful, Is - n't

Je - sus my Lord won-der - ful! Eyes have seen, ears have heard, 'Tis re -

cord - ed in God's Word. Is - n't Je - sus my Lord won-der - ful!

Turn Your Eyes upon Jesus

H.H.L.   HELEN H. LEMMEL

Turn your eyes up-on Je - sus, Look full in His

won - der - ful face,_____ And the things of earth will grow

strange - ly dim In the light of His glo - ry and grace.

Every Moment of the Day

H.D.L.

HARRY DIXON LOES

Ev - 'ry mo-ment of the day_____ My Fa - ther cares for

me,_____ Ev - 'ry mo -ment of the day_____ My heart from fear is

free;_____ He who sees the spar - row fall_____ Will hear my call:_____

_____ Ev - 'ry mo-ment of the day God watch-es o - ver me._____

He's the Savior of My Soul

Traditional

Latin American melody

He's the Sav - ior of my soul— My Je - sus, my

Je - sus. He's the Sav - ior of my soul,— He's the

Sav - ior of my soul.— Je - sus, Je -

sus, Je - sus, Je - sus. He's the Sav - ior of my

soul,— He's the Sav - ior of my soul.—

Give Them All to Jesus

P.J. & B.B.

PHIL JOHNSON & BOB BENSON

Give them all, give them all, Give them all to Je-sus:__ Shat-tered dreams, wound-ed hearts,__ bro-ken toys.

Give them all, give them all, Give them all to Je-sus__ And__ He will turn your sor-row in-to joy.

I Just Keep Trusting My Lord

J.W.P.

JOHN W. PETERSON

I just keep trust-ing my Lord _____ as I walk a - long, _____

I just keep trust-ing my Lord _____ and He gives a song; _____

Tho the storm-clouds dark-en the sky _____ o'er the heav'n-ly trail, _____

Fine

I just keep trust - ing my Lord — _____ He will nev - er fail! _____

He's a faith - ful Friend, _____ such a faith - ful Friend, _____

D.S. al Fine

I can count on Him to the ver - y end;

Born Again

MERRILL DUNLOP

M.D.

Born a - gain, born a - gain, Tru - ly I've been born a - gain,

Saved by the blood of the Lamb I am And I know I'm born a - gain.

Born a - gain, born a - gain, Tru - ly I've been born a - gain,

Saved by the blood of the Lamb I am And I know I'm born a - gain!

For God So Loved the World

1–ELDON BURKWALL
2–FRANCES TOWNSEND
3–Source unknown

ALFRED B. SMITH

1. He came un-to His own— His own re-ceived Him not, But all who
2. For God so loved the world He gave His on - ly Son To die on
3. If God so loved the world Then we should love it too, And strive to

will be - lieve The pow - er will re - ceive To be the sons of God
Cal - v'ry's tree, From sin to set me free; Some - day He's com-ing back—
live for Him, Lost sin - ners seek to win, So they'll be read - y when

By trust - ing in His name: I'm so glad that Je - sus came!____
What glo - ry that will be: Won - der-ful His love to me!____
He comes to earth a - gain: Joy - ful will that meet - ing be!____

If You Want Joy

J.D.C.

JOSEPH D. CARLSON

Brightly

If you want joy, real joy, won-der-ful joy,_____ Let Je - sus come
true joy,

in - to your heart;_____ heart._____ Your sins He'll wash a - way,
your heart; your heart.

Your night He'll turn to day, Your life He'll make it o - ver a - new;_____
a - new;

Walking with Jesus

Source unknown

Walk - ing with Je - sus— Walk-ing ev - 'ry day, walk-ing all the way;

Walk - ing with Je - sus— Walk - ing with Je - sus a - lone.

*NOTE: The audience may divide into two groups, one group singing the following counter melody on the measures bracketed above, then merging again with the other voices.

Walk - ing in the sun - light, walk - ing in the shad - ow.

Worthy Is the Lamb

From Revelation 5: 12

DON WYRTZEN

Wor - thy is the Lamb that was slain. Wor - thy is the Lamb that was slain. Wor - thy is the Lamb that was slain, to re - ceive: Pow - er and rich - es and wis - dom and strength, Hon - or and glo - ry and bless - ing! Wor - thy is the Lamb, Wor - thy is the Lamb, Wor - thy is the

Lamb that was slain,———— Wor - thy is the Lamb!————

He's the One I Love

Source unknown
Arr. by Merrill Dunlop

He's the One I love in the morn-ing, He's the One I love at noon;

He's the One at eve-ning twi-light, He's the One at mid-night gloom;

He's the Oak and I'm the i-vy, He's the Pot-ter, I'm the clay;

For my Lord and me there'll nev-er be A part-ing day.

Jesus, Wonderful Lord

P.W.

PAUL WHITE

Flowing, moderately slow

Je - sus, ____ name a - bove all names, ____ Beau - ti - ful Sav - ior, ____ glo - ri - ous Lord. ____ Em - man - u - el, ____ God ___ is with us; ____ Bless - ed Re - deem - er, ____ Liv - ing Word. ____

Where the Spirit Of the Lord Is

From II Corinthians 3: 17

STEPHEN R. ADAMS

Surely Goodness and Mercy

J.W.P. & A.B.S.

JOHN W. PETERSON & ALFRED B. SMITH

Sure-ly good-ness and mer-cy shall fol - low_ me All the days, all the days of my life.___ Sure-ly good-ness and mer-cy shall fol - low_ me All the days, all the days of my life.___ And I shall dwell in the house of the Lord for - ev - er, And I shall feast at the ta-ble spread for me.___ Sure-ly good-ness and

mer - cy shall fol - low_ me All the days, all the days of my

life;_____ All the days, all the days of my life._____

When We See Christ

E.K.R.

ESTHER KERR RUSTHOI

It will be worth it all_____ When we see Je - sus,_____ Life's trials will

seem so small_____ When we see Christ;_____ One glimpse of His dear face_____ All

sor - row will e - rase,_____ So brave-ly run the race_____ Till we see Christ._____

Brighten the Corner

INA DULEY OGDON

CHARLES H. GABRIEL

Bright-en the cor-ner where you are! Bright-en the cor-ner

where you are! Some-one far from har-bor you may

guide a - cross the bar, Bright-en the cor-ner where you are.

My Sins Are Gone

H.G.

HELEN GRIGGS

Gone, gone, gone, gone! Yes, my sins are gone. Now my soul is free, and in my

heart's a song; Bur-ied in the deep-est sea, Yes, that's good e-nough for me;

rit.

I shall live e - ter - nal - ly, Praise God! My sins are gone!

Jesus, We Just Want to Thank You

W.J. & GLORIA GAITHER

WILLIAM J. GAITHER

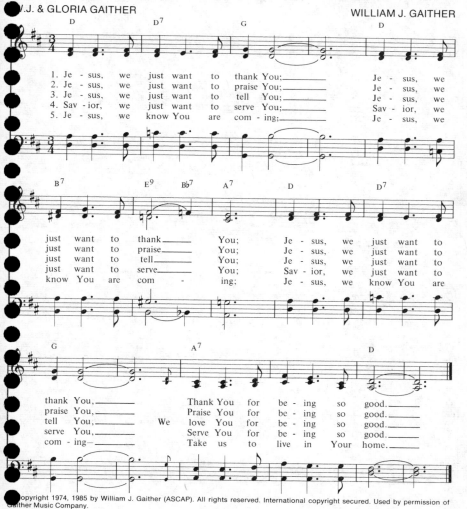

1. Je - sus, we just want to thank You;____ Je - sus, we
2. Je - sus, we just want to praise You;____ Je - sus, we
3. Je - sus, we just want to tell You;____ Je - sus, we
4. Sav - ior, we just want to serve You;____ Sav - ior, we
5. Je - sus, we know You are com - ing;____ Je - sus, we

just want to thank____ You; Je - sus, we just want to
just want to praise____ You; Je - sus, we just want to
just want to tell____ You; Je - sus, we just want to
just want to serve____ You; Sav - ior, we just want to
know You are com - ing; Je - sus, we know You are

thank You,____ Thank You for be - ing so good.____
praise You,____ Praise You for be - ing so good.____
tell You,____ We love You for be - ing so good.____
serve You,____ Serve You for be - ing so good.____
com - ing____ Take us to live in Your home.____

Nothing Is Impossible

E.L.C.

EUGENE L. CLARK

Noth-ing is im-pos-si-ble when you put your trust in God;

Noth-ing is im-pos-si-ble when you're trust-ing in His Word.

Heark-en to the voice of God to thee: "Is there an-y-thing too

hard for Me?" Then put your trust in God a-lone and

rest up-on His Word— For ev-'ry-thing, O ev-'ry-thing,

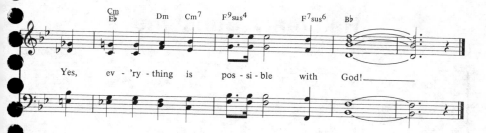

Yes, ev - 'ry - thing is pos - si - ble with God!___

Every Moment of Every Day

N.J.C.

NORMAN J. CLAYTON

On - ly to be what He wants me to be, Ev - 'ry mo-ment of ev - 'ry day;___

Yield - ed com-plete-ly to Je - sus a - lone, Ev - 'ry step of this pil - grim way.___

Just to be clay in the Pot - ter's hands, Read - y to do what His Word com-mands,

On - ly to be what He wants me to be, Ev - 'ry mo-ment of ev - 'ry day.___

79

Heavenly Sunshine

Traditional

Heav-en-ly sun-shine, heav-en-ly sun-shine, Flood-ing my soul with glo-ry di-vine!___ Heav-en-ly sun-shine, heav-en-ly sun-shine, Hal-le-lu-jah! Je-sus is mine!___

Wonderful, Wonderful Jesus

B.A.B.

BENJAMIN A. BAUR

Won-der-ful, won-der-ful Je - sus! He is my friend, true to the end; He gave Him-self to re - deem___ me—___ Je - sus, won-der-ful Lord!___

80

Morning Song

B.Y.

BILL YARGER

1. Je - sus, how I need You As the day be -
2. And, Je - sus, in the eve - ning, Draw my thoughts to

gins; Let me glo - ri - fy You— Keep me, Lord, from
You; Fill my heart with praise, — Lord, And thanks-giv - ing,

sin. When the pres - sure ris - es With the pass - ing
too. Guide me through the dark - ness— Keep me, Lord, from

day, Give me strength to fol - low,
harm; May the morn - ing find me

1
Help me to o - bey.

D.C. 2
Rest-ing in Your arms.

Simple Gifts

G   D⁷   G Shaker hymn

'Tis a gift to be sim - ple, 'tis a gift to be free, 'Tis a

gift to come down where we ought to be; And when we find our -

selves in the place just right, 'Twill be in the val - ley of

love and de - light. When true sim - plic - i - ty is gained, To

bow and to bend we__ shan't be a - shamed; To turn, turn will

be our de-light, Till by turn-ing, turn-ing we come round right.

Every Day with Jesus

ROBERT C. LOVELESS   WENDELL P. LOVELESS

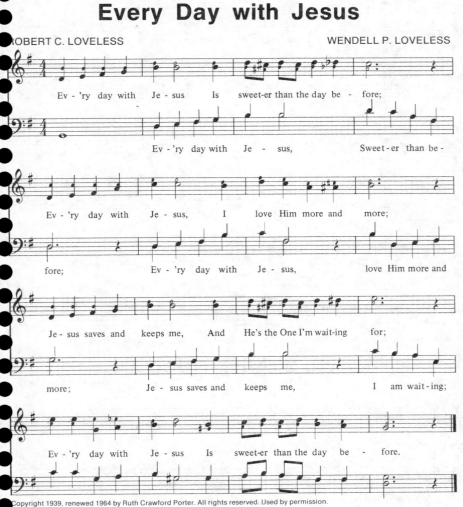

Ev-'ry day with Je-sus Is sweet-er than the day be-fore;

Ev-'ry day with Je-sus, Sweet-er than be-

Ev-'ry day with Je-sus, I love Him more and more;

fore; Ev-'ry day with Je-sus, love Him more and

Je-sus saves and keeps me, And He's the One I'm wait-ing for;

more; Je-sus saves and keeps me, I am wait-ing;

Ev-'ry day with Je-sus Is sweet-er than the day be-fore.

Every Day's a Happy Day

R.C.L.

ROBERT C. LOVELESS

Ev - 'ry day's a hap - py day With Je - sus in my heart,

Just to know as on we go That we shall nev - er part. Praise God!

Je - sus Christ, my Sav - ior, paid it all on Cal - va - ry, And

that's the rea - son why I am so hap - py. I am free.

He's All I Need

Source unknown

He's all I need, He's all I need, Je - sus is all I need; ___

Praise Him
(Jesus in the Morning)

Traditional

Learning to Lean

J.S.

JOHN STALLINGS

Learn-ing to lean, _____ learn-ing to lean, I'm learn-ing to lean on Je - sus. _____ Find-ing more pow-er than I'd ev - er dreamed, I'm learn-ing to lean on Je - sus.

1. A joy I can't ex-plain _____ is fill-ing my soul Since the day I met Je - sus, my King. _____ His bless - ed Ho-ly Spir - it is
2. There's glo - ri - ous vic-t'ry each day now for me As I dwell in His peace so se - rene. _____ He helps me with each task _____ if

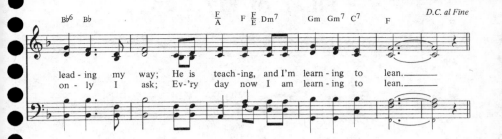

lead - ing my way; He is teach - ing, and I'm learn - ing to lean.
on - ly I ask; Ev - 'ry day now I am learn - ing to lean.

We Will Worship at His Feet

PHIL POSTHUMA

P.P.

We will wor - ship ___ at His feet, ___ we'll fall on our knees; ___ With

all the saints a - round the throne, we'll join in and sing ___

Sweet ___ hal - le - lu - jahs that nev - er will cease, And we'll be re -

joic - ing ___ as we lift up our King ___ at His feet. ___

8va

87

Filler of My Cup

B.Y.

BILL YARGER

(Descant ends 2nd time)

Lyrics:

Je - sus, fill my cup; Lord, I lift it up. With Your love re - store; Fill my cup once more.

Flow - ing from with - in, Fill my soul a - gain. With Your love re - new;

Je - sus, fill-er of my cup, Lord, I lift it up. Je - sus, with Your love re - store; Lord Je - sus, fill-er of my cup.

Je - sus, flow-ing from with - in, fill my soul a - gain. Je - sus, with Your love re - new; Lord Je - sus, fill my cup with You.

(Sing melody, 2nd time)

If You Abide in Me

Based on John 15:5-7

GEORGE CASTADY

If you a - bide in Me and My words a - bide in you, You shall ask what you will and it

1 Repeat both times **2** to next bar, 1st time / Fine, 2nd time

shall be done to you. If shall be done to you.

I am the true Vine, you are the bran - ches; A-

D.S.

part from Me you can do noth - ing at all. If

89

Summertime in My Heart

L.C.J.

LOIS C. JOHNSON

It is sum-mer-time in my heart, Yes, it's sum-mer-time in my heart;___ Since Je - sus saved me, New life He gave me. E - ven in win-ter-time it's sum-mer in my heart! It is sum-mer-time in my heart, Yes, it's sum-mer-time in my heart;___ Since Je - sus saved me, New life He gave me. E-ven in win - ter-time it's sum-mer in my

heart! It is sum-mer-time in my heart, Yes, it's

sum-mer-time in my heart;_____ Since Je-sus saved me, New life He

gave me. E-ven in win-ter-time it's sum-mer in my heart!

Thank You, Lord

S. & B.S. SETH & BESSIE SYKES

Thank You, Lord, for sav-ing my soul; Thank You, Lord, for mak-ing me whole;

Thank You, Lord, for giv-ing to me Thy great sal-va-tion so rich and free.

I Shall Not Be Moved

Verses by JOHN T. BENSON

Traditional melody
Arr. by Mrs. James Pate

I shall not be, I shall not be moved; I shall not be, I shall not be moved; Just like a tree that's plant-ed by the wa-ters, Lord, I shall not be moved (be moved).

O He's Done So Much for Me

Traditional

Oh ——— He's done so much for me; Oh, ——— He's done so much for me; Oh, ——— He's done so much for me; I nev-er can for-get all He's done for me.

Come, Holy Spirit

W.J. & GLORIA GAITHER

WILLIAM J. GAITHER

Come, Ho-ly Spir - it, I need You;_____ Come, sweet

Spir - it, I pray;_____ Come, in Your strength and Your

pow - er;_____ Come,___ in Your own gen - tle way.

The Love of God

F.M.L.

FREDERICK M. LEHMAN

Oh, love of God, how rich and pure!__How mea-sure - less___ and strong!

It shall for - ev - er-more en - dure__ The saints' and an - gels' song.

93

We Are More than Conquerors

R.C.

RALPH CARMICHAEL

We are more than con-quer-ors through Him that loved us so. The Christ who dwells with-in us is the great-est pow'r we know. He will fight be-side us the e-ne-my is great; Who can stand a-gainst us— He's the Cap-tain of our fate. Then we will con-quer, nev-er fear, so let the bat-tle rage.

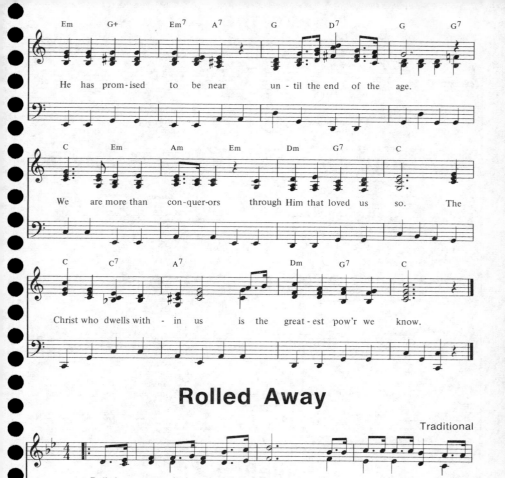

He has prom-ised to be near un-til the end of the age.

We are more than con-quer-ors through Him that loved us so. The

Christ who dwells with - in us is the great-est pow'r we know.

Rolled Away

Traditional

Rolled a - way, rolled a-way, rolled a - way, Ev-'ry bur-den of my heart rolled a-

Fine

D.C. al Fine

way! Ev-'ry sin had to go 'Neath the crim - son flow, hal-le-lu-jah!

I Have the Joy

Traditional
Arr. by Harry Dixon Loes

1. I have the joy,— joy,— joy,— joy— down in my heart,
2. I have the peace that pass - eth un - der-stand-ing down in my heart,
3. I have the love of Je - sus, love of Je - sus down in my heart,

Down in my heart, down in my heart; I have the joy,— joy,—
Down in my heart, down in my heart; I have the peace that pass - eth
Down in my heart, down in my heart; I have the love of Je - sus,

joy,— joy— down in my heart, Down in my heart to stay.—
un - der-stand-ing down in my heart, Down in my heart to stay.—
love of Je - sus down in my heart, Down in my heart to stay.—

Alleluia

J.S.
JERRY SINCLAIR

p 1. Al - le - lu - ia, Al - le - lu - ia, Al - le - lu - ia, Al - le - lu - ia,
mp 2. He's my Sav - ior, He's my Sav - ior, He's my Sav - ior, He's my Sav - ior,
mf 3. He is wor - thy, He is wor - thy, He is wor - thy, He is wor - thy,
f 4. I will praise Him, I will praise Him, I will praise Him, I will praise Him,

Al - le - lu - ia, Al - le - lu - ia, Al - le - lu - ia, Al - le - lu - ia!
He's my Sav - ior, He's my Sav - ior, He's my Sav - ior, He's my Sav - ior!
He is wor - thy, He is wor - thy, He is wor - thy, He is wor - thy!
I will praise Him, I will praise Him, I will praise Him, I will praise Him!

Were You There?

Traditional

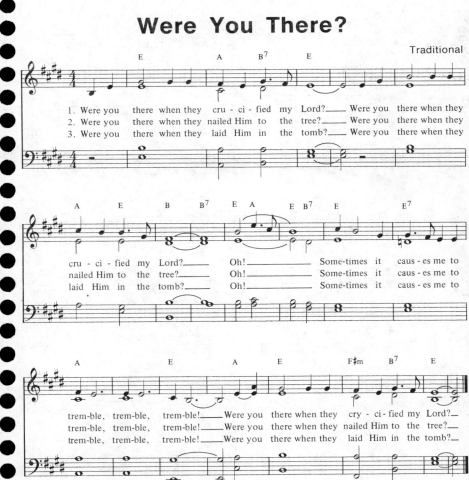

1. Were you there when they cru - ci - fied my Lord?____ Were you there when they
2. Were you there when they nailed Him to the tree?____ Were you there when they
3. Were you there when they laid Him in the tomb?____ Were you there when they

cru - ci - fied my Lord?____ Oh!____ Some-times it caus - es me to
nailed Him to the tree?____ Oh!____ Some-times it caus - es me to
laid Him in the tomb?____ Oh!____ Some-times it caus - es me to

trem-ble, trem-ble, trem-ble!____Were you there when they cry - ci - fied my Lord?__
trem-ble, trem-ble, trem-ble!____Were you there when they nailed Him to the tree?__
trem-ble, trem-ble, trem-ble!____Were you there when they laid Him in the tomb?__

Optional 4.—Were you there when He rose up from the grave?

97

He's Everything to Me

R.C.

RALPH CARMICHAEL

In the stars His hand-i - work I see,
On the wind He speaks with
I will cel - e - brate Na - tiv - i - ty,
For it has a place in

maj - es - ty;
Though He rul - eth o - ver land and sea,
his - to - ry;
Sure, He came to set His peo - ple free—

What is that to me?
What is that to me?

Till by faith I met Him face to face
And I felt the won-der of His grace—

Then I knew that He was more than just a God who did-n't care, that

98

lived a - way out there; And now He walks be-side me day by day, Ev-er

watch-ing o'er me lest I stray, Help-ing me to find that nar - row way—

1 He's ev-'ry-thing to me.

2 He's ev - 'ry - thing to me!____

Into Thy Presence

Source unknown

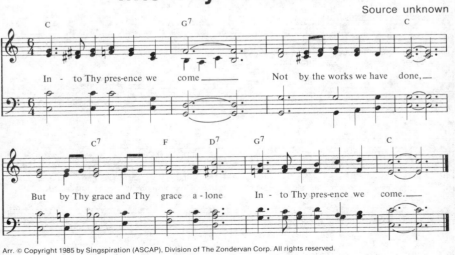

In - to Thy pres-ence we come____ Not by the works we have done,__

But by Thy grace and Thy grace a - lone In - to Thy pres-ence we come.__

Everybody Ought to Know

Source unknown

REFRAIN
sing first refrain twice

Ev-'ry-bod-y ought to know,____ Ev-'ry-bod-y ought to know,____

____ Ev-'ry-bod-y ought to know____ Who Je - sus is.____

Fine

STANZAS

1. He's the Lil - y of the Val - ley, He's the
2. On the cross He died for sin - ners, And His

Bright and Morn - ing Star;____ He's the fair - est of ten
blood makes white as snow;____ Lov - ing, liv - ing, com-ing

D.C.

thou - sand— Ev - 'ry - bod - y ought to know.____
Sav - ior— He's the one you ought to know.____

He Is the Way

OTIS SKILLINGS

O.S.

1. God sent His Son to be our Sav - ior, God sent His Son to be our Sav - ior, God sent His Son to
2. 'Twas Je - sus Christ who came to save the world,'Twas Je - sus Christ who came to save the world,'Twas Je - sus Christ who

1-5
be our Sav - ior: He is the Way, He is the Truth, He is the Life.
came to save the world: He is the

6 - final (optional)
Way, He is the Truth, He is the Life!

3. He gave His life that we might be set free . . .
4. Rose from the grave that we might live again . . .
5. He lives today—I know He always will . . .
6. God sent His Son to be our Savior . . .

101

He Loves, He Saves, He Keeps

WILLIAM M. RUNYAN

WENDELL P. LOVELESS

He loves, He saves, He keeps, He sat-is-fies This long-ing heart of mine;

He fills my life to o - ver-flow-ing With His joy and peace di - vine.

He guides, He guards, He watch - es o-ver me, He slum-bers not nor sleeps;

For He is my glo - rious Sav - ior, And He loves, He saves, He keeps.

This One Thing I Know

S.C.

SIDNEY COX

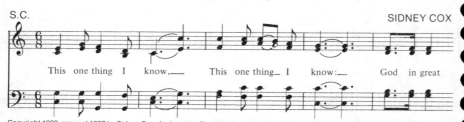

This one thing I know,___ This one thing_ I know:___ God in great

mer - cy par - doned me, (He) Snapped sin's fet - ters and set___ me free.

Once I was blind___ but now I see— This one thing___ I know!___

After All He's Done for Me

BETSY DAASVAND   WENDELL P. LOVELESS

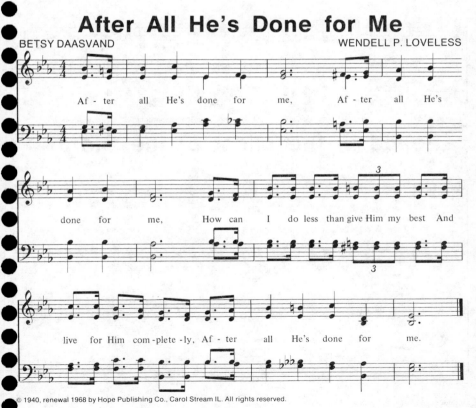

Af - ter all He's done for me, Af - ter all He's

done for me, How can I do less than give Him my best And

live for Him com - plete - ly, Af - ter all He's done for me.

Because He Lives

W.J. & GLORIA GAITHER

WILLIAM J. GAITHER

Be - cause He lives____ I can face to - mor - row. Be-cause He lives____

____ all fear is gone.____ Be - cause I know____ He holds the

fu - ture____ And life is worth the liv - ing— just be-cause He lives.

Peace in the Midst of the Storm

S.R.A.

STEPHEN R. ADAMS

There is peace in the midst of my storm-tossed life; Oh, there's an An - chor,

there's a Rock to cast my faith up-on. ____ Je - sus rides in my ves-sel____

so I'll fear no a - larm; He gives me peace in the midst of my storm!__

All Day Song
(Love Him in the Morning)

J.F.

JOHN FISHER

Love Him in the morn - in' when you see the sun a - ris - in',

Love Him in the eve - nin' 'cause He took you thru the day.

And in the in - be-tween time when you feel the pres - sure com - in',

Re - mem-ber that He loves you, and He prom - is - es to stay.

Got Any Rivers?

O.E.

OSCAR ELIASON

Got an - y riv - ers you think are un - cross - a - ble? Got an - y
moun - tains you can't tun - nel thru? God spe - cial - iz - es in
things tho't im - pos - si - ble; He does the things oth - ers can - not do.

Hallelujah!

Traditional

Hal - le - lu, hal - le - lu, hal - le - lu, hal - le - lu - jah! Praise ye the Lord! Hal - le -
lu, hal - le - lu, hal - le - lu, hal - le - lu - jah! Praise ye the Lord! Praise ye the Lord, hal - le - lu - jah!

Praise ye the Lord, hal-le-lu-jah! Praise ye the Lord, hal-le-lu-jah! Praise ye the Lord!

Life Is a Symphony

B.B.B.

BEATRICE BUSH BIXLER

Life is a sym-pho-ny, Since the Man of Gal-i-lee

Changed my dis-cords in-to song, Made life sweet the whole day long.

Life is a sym-pho-ny, Praise the Man of Gal-i-lee!

No more a stran-ger—He is the ar-ran-ger of my sym-pho-ny!____

I Have Decided to Follow Jesus

Attributed to an Indian Prince

Folk melody from India

1. I have de - cid - ed___ to fol - low Je - sus.___ I have de - cid - ed___
2. Tho no one join me,___ still I will fol - low.___ Tho no one join me,___
3. The world be - hind me,___ the cross be - fore me. ___ The world be - hind me,___

to fol - low Je - sus.___ I have de - cid - ed___ to fol - low Je - sus—
still I will fol - low.___ Tho no one join me,___ still I will fol - low—
the cross be - fore me.___ The world be - hind me, ___ the cross be - fore me—

No turn - ing back, (No turn - ing back,) no turn - ing back.___

On the Victory Side

W.J.M.

WALTER J. MAIN

On the vic - t'ry side, On the vic - t'ry side; No foe can daunt me,

No fear can haunt me On the vic-t'ry side. On the vic-t'ry side, On the

vic-t'ry side! With Christ with-in, The fight we'll win, On the vic-t'ry side!

I Just Came to Praise the Lord

W.R.

WAYNE ROMERO

1. I just came to praise the Lord. I just came to praise the
2. I just came to thank the Lord. I just came to thank the

Lord. I just came to praise His
Lord. I just came to praise His

Ho - ly Name: I just came to praise the Lord.
Ho - ly Name: I just came to thank the Lord.

There's a New Song in My Heart

J.W.P.

JOHN W. PETERSON

There's a new song in my heart since the Sav-ior set me free; There's a new song in my heart— 'tis a heav'n-ly har-mo-ny! All my sins are washed a-way in the blood of Cal-va-ry; O what peace and joy noth-ing can de-stroy—There's a new song in my heart!

The Name of Jesus

W. C. MARTIN

EDMUND S. LORENZ

"Je - sus"— O how sweet the name, "Je - sus"—ev-'ry day the same;

"Je - sus"— let all saints pro-claim Its wor - thy praise for - ev - er!
Its wor - thy praise

The Longer I Serve Him

W.J.G.

WILLIAM J. GAITHER

The long - er I serve Him the sweet - er He grows; The

more that I love Him, more love He be - stows. Each

day is like heav - en, my heart o - ver - flows; The

long - er I serve__ Him the sweet - er He grows.__

Jesus Is Worthy of Praise

L.P.L.

LOUIS P. LEHMAN

Je - sus is wor - thy of praise; _____ Je - sus is wor - thy of praise. _____ The Lamb who was slain for - ev - er shall reign, And Je - sus is wor - thy of praise. _____

Mansion over the Hilltop

I.S.

IRA STANPHILL

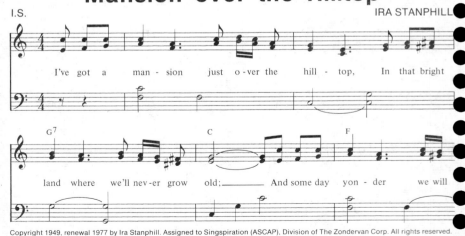

I've got a man - sion just o - ver the hill - top, In that bright land where we'll nev - er grow old; _____ And some day yon - der we will

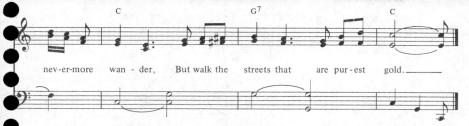

nev-er-more wan-der, But walk the streets that are pur-est gold.____

Sing when the Day Is Bright

Traditional

Sing____ when the day is bright, Sing____ thru the dark-est night; Ev-'ry

day,____ all the way,____ Let us sing, sing, sing!

Sing____ when the day is bright, Sing____ thru the dark-est night; Ev-'ry

day,____ all the way,____ Let us sing! sing! sing!

I Will Sing of the Mercies of the Lord

From Psalm 89:1

J. H. FILLMORE
Arr. by David Culross

The Adoration

J.E.P.

JOE E. PARKS

1. Just like the wise-men, Je-sus, we a-dore You,
2. Just like the wise-men, Je-sus, we would love You,
3. Just like the wise-men, Je-sus, we would praise You,

Just like the wise-men we bow be-fore You;
There is no oth-er on earth a-bove You;
With hearts and voic-es we would up-raise You;

This is our of-fer-ing, our lives to You we bring,
Come, be our hon-ored guest, Your name be ev-er blest,
At this glad Christ-mas-tide now in our hearts a-bide,

Prais-es we tru-ly sing, O Son of God, di-vine.
In us be man-i'-fest, O Son of God, di-vine.

Come, be our friend and guide, O Son of God, di-vine.

Cheer Up, Ye Saints of God

Source unknown

Cheer up, ye saints of God, There's noth-ing to wor-ry a-bout, Noth-ing to make you feel a-fraid; Noth-ing to make you doubt._ Re - mem-ber Je - sus nev-er fails, So why not trust Him and shout! You'll be sor-ry you wor-ried at all to-mor-row morn - ing.

I'll Praise Your Name, Lord

P. & L.B.

DON WYRTZEN, PHIL & LYNNE BROWER

I'll praise Your name, Lord,_ and sing Your song;_ I'll praise Your name, Lord,_ my whole life long;_ I'll praise Your name, Lord,_ un-til I'm

home;_____ I'll praise Your name, Lord,_____ and sing Your song._____

O How He Loves You and Me!

K.K.

KURT KAISER

1. O how He loves you and me,_____ O how He
2. Je - sus to Cal - v'ry did go,_____ His love for

loves you and me;_____ He gave His life— what__
man - kind to show;_____ What He did there bro't__

more could He give? O how He loves you, O how He
hope from de - spair: O how He loves you, O how He

loves me, O how He loves you and me!_____
loves me, O how He loves you and me!_____

Everyone, Everywhere

L.P.L.

LOUIS P. LEHMAN

Ev - 'ry-one, ev - 'ry-where, real - ly ought to know how God loves him,

Ev - 'ry-one, ev - 'ry-where, real - ly ought to know how God loves him,

Ev - 'ry - one should know he's in God's lov - ing thought,

Ev - 'ry - one should know what the blood has bought, and

Ev - 'ry - one, ev - 'ry-where, real - ly ought to know how God loves him.

The Family of God

W.J. & GLORIA GAITHER

WILLIAM J. GAITHER

I'm so glad I'm a part of the fam - 'ly of God—

I've been washed in the foun - tain, cleansed by His

blood! Joint heirs with Je - sus as we trav - el this

slower, 2nd time

sod— For I'm part of the fam - 'ly, the fam - 'ly of

God. _____ I'm so God. _____

How Great Thou Art

CARL BOBERG
Trans. by Stuart Hine

Swedish melody

Then sings my soul, my Sav - ior God, to Thee;____ How great Thou art,____ how great Thou art!____ Then sings my soul, my Sav - ior God, to Thee;____ How great Thou art, ____ how great Thou art!____

Bless His Holy Name

A.C.

ANDRAÉ CROUCH

Bless the Lord, O my soul, And all that is with - in me bless His ho - ly ____ name. He has done great things, ____ He has done great

things,____ He has done great things, bless His ho - ly name.

My Lord Knows the Way

S.E.C.

SIDNEY E. COX

My Lord knows the way thru the wil-der-ness— All I have to do is fol - low; My

Lord knows the way thru the wil - der - ness— All I have to do is fol - low.

Strength for to-day is mine all the way, And all I need for to - mor - row! My

Lord knows the way thru the wil - der-ness— All I have to do is fol - low.

Jesus, Lord to Me

G.M. & G.N.

GARY McSPADDEN & GREG NELSON

Je - sus, Je - sus, Lord to me; Mas - ter,

Sav - ior, Prince of Peace. Ru - ler of my

heart to - day, Je - sus, Lord to me.

I Believe, Lord

L.P.L.

LOUIS P. LEHMAN

I be - lieve, Lord— I re - ceive, Lord, All that Cal - v'ry bought—all that grace has brought;

I be - lieve, Lord—_ I be - lieve! All that Je - sus pur - chased I re - ceive.

He Is Worthy/
Praise the Name of the Lord

Words from Rev. 5:12 and D.C.

DON WYRTZEN ,PHIL & LYNNE BROWER
and DAVID CULROSS

† Sing melody 1st time. Sing descant 2nd time. Sing *both* melody and descant 3rd time.

123

Let the Beauty of Jesus Be Seen in Me

ALBERT W. T. ORSBORN

TOM JONES

Let the beau-ty of Je-sus be seen in me—

All His won-der-ful pas-sion and pu - ri - ty!

O Thou Spir - it di -vine, All my na - ture re -fine.

Till the beau-ty of Je - sus be seen in me._____

Burdens Are Lifted at Calvary

J.M.M.

JOHN M. MOORE

Bur-dens are lift - ed at Cal - va -ry, Cal - va -ry,_____ Cal - va -ry;

Bur - dens are lift - ed at Cal - va - ry, Je - sus is ver - y near. / ver - y near.

I Am Loved

W.J. & G.G.

WILLIAM J. GAITHER

I am loved, I am loved, I can risk lov - ing you;

For the One who knows me best loves me most.

I am loved, I am loved; won't you please take my

hand? We are free to love each oth - er, we are loved.

His Name Is Wonderful

A.M.

AUDREY MIEIR

His name is Won-der-ful, His name is Won-der-ful, His name is Won-der-ful, Je-sus, my Lord; He is the might-y King, Mas-ter of ev-'ry-thing, His name is Won-der-ful, Je-sus, my Lord. He's the great Shep-herd, the Rock of all a - ges, Al - might - y God is He; Bow down be - fore Him, Love and a -

dore Him, His name is Won-der-ful, Je-sus my Lord.

Spirit of the Living God

D.I.

DANIEL IVERSON

Spir - it of the Liv-ing God, fall fresh on me! Spir - it of the

Liv - ing God, fall fresh on me! Melt me, mold me,

much slower to end

fill me, use me! Spir - it of the Liv-ing God, fall fresh on me!

Something Beautiful

GLORIA GAITHER   WILLIAM J. GAITHER

Some - thing beau - ti - ful, some - thing good;
All my con - fu - sion He un - der - stood.
All I had to of - fer Him was bro - ken - ness and
strife, But He made some - thing beau - ti - ful of my life.

Isn't the Love of Jesus Something Wonderful?

J.W.P.   JOHN W. PETERSON

Is-n't the love of Je - sus some-thing won - der - ful, won - der - ful, won - der - ful;

128

O is-n't the love of Je - sus some-thing won - der - ful! Won-der-ful it is to me.

Through It All

ANDRAE CROUCH

A.C.

Through it all,_____ Through it all,_____ Oh, I've

learned to trust in Je - sus, I've learned to trust in God.

Through it all,_____ Through it all,_____ I've

learned to de - pend up - on His Word.

How Majestic Is Your Name

M.W.S.

MICHAEL W. SMITH

God— O— Lord— God Al - might - y!—

New Life!

J.W.P.   JOHN W. PETERSON

New life in Christ!— A - bun - dant and free!— What

Play melody and bass in octaves.

glo - ries shine, What joys are mine, What won - drous bless-ings I see!— My

past with its sin,— The search - ing and strife,— For-

ev - er gone—There's a bright new dawn! For in Christ I have found new life!—

We Will Glorify

T.P.

TWILA PARIS

1. We will glo-ri-fy the King of Kings, We will glo-ri-fy the Lamb;
(2. Lord Je-) ho-vah reigns in maj-es-ty, We will bow be-fore His throne;

We will glo-ri-fy the Lord of Lords, Who is the great I
We will wor-ship Him in right-eous-ness, We will wor-ship Him a-

lone. 3. He is Lord of heav-en, Lord of earth, He is
lu-jah to the King of Kings, Hal-le-
glo-ri-fy the King of Kings, We will

Lord of all who live; He is Lord a-bove the
lu-jah to the Lamb; Hal-le-lu-jah to the
glo-ri-fy the Lamb; We will glo-ri-fy the

u-ni-verse— All praise to Him we give. 4. O hal-le-
Lord of Lords, Who is the great I Am. 5. We will
Lord of Lords, Who is the great I Am.

INDEX